BOY, IF YOU WEREN'T A GIRL...

C'MON..I'M READY FOR YOU! PUT 'EM UP THERE !!

Very Funny,

Selected Cartoons from
YOU'RE OUT OF YOUR MIND,
CHARLIE BROWN
Vol. 1

Charlie Brown

by Charles M. Schulz

A Fawcett Crest Book
Fawcett Publications, Inc., Greenwich, Conn.
Member of American Book Publishers Council, Inc.

VERY FUNNY, CHARLIE BROWN

This book, prepared especially for Fawcett Publications, Inc., comprises the first half of YOU'RE OUT OF YOUR MIND, CHARLIE BROWN!, and is published by arrangement with Holt, Rinehart and Winston, Inc.

PRINTING HISTORY

First Holt, Rinehart and Winston printing, February 1959
Ninth printing, April 1964

First Fawcett Crest printing, January 1965
Second printing, June 1965
Third printing, October 1965
Fourth printing, November 1965
Fifth printing, July 1966

Published by Fawcett World Library,
67 West 44th Street, New York, N. Y. 10036
Printed in the United States of America

MY BLANKET IS IN THE DRYER..HOW LONG DO YOU THINK IT'LL TAKE TO GET DRY?
HOW IN THE WORLD SHOULD I KNOW?
I GOTTA HAVE THAT BLANKET..
SIGH
THIS IS A LONELY VIGIL....

NO!
OH, COME ON, CHARLIE BROWN..
I'LL HOLD IT REAL STEADY...
NO!
PLEASE?
NO! YOU JUST WANT ME TO COME RUNNING UP TO KICK THAT BALL SO YOU CAN PULL IT AWAY AND SEE ME KILL MYSELF!
LOOK...JUST TO SHOW YOU I'M SINCERE, I'LL GIVE YOU A MILLION DOLLARS IF I PULL THE BALL AWAY!
IN FACT, I'LL GIVE YOU A HUNDRED MILLION DOLLARS!!
I MUST BE OUT OF MY MIND, BUT I CAN'T RESIST KICKING FOOTBALLS..

HA!
WHAM
HERE'S YOUR MONEY, CHARLIE BROWN!
HEE HEE HEE HEE HEE HEE
I THINK I'LL JUST LIE HERE UNTIL THE FIRST SNOW COMES AND COVERS ME UP...
SCHULZ

DISGRACEFUL!
OH, GO AWAY!
COMPLETELY DISGRACEFUL!
YOU AND THAT STUPID BLANKET! ARE YOU GONNA CARRY THAT THING AROUND THE REST OF YOUR LIFE?
WHEN ARE YOU GOING TO LEARN TO STAND ON YOUR OWN TWO FEET?
WADDYA MEAN?!

I'VE GOT JUST AS MUCH WILL POWER AS ANYONE ELSE! SEE? I DON'T NEED THIS BLANKET! I CAN THROW IT AWAY ANYTIME I WANT TO! ANYTIME!
GOOD GRIEF!
YOU'RE A HOPELESS CASE, LINUS...
I THOUGHT I COULD DO IT... I ACTUALLY THOUGHT I COULD DO IT...
SCHULZ

GEE, IT WOULD BE NICE TO BE A BIRD!
THEN, IF YOU WEREN'T SATISFIED WHERE YOU WERE, YOU COULD..
..TAKE OFF!
AND THEN IF YOU WEREN'T SATISFIED THERE, YOU COULD TAKE OFF AGAIN!

ZOOM!
ZOOM!
ZOOM!
WHEW
I'M NOT SURE I COULD STAND ALL THAT ZOOMING..
SCHULZ

AH...AH....
!
AHHHH...
TURN YOUR HEAD!
TURN YOUR HEAD!
AHCHOO!
SCHULZ

SCHROEDER, DO PIANO PLAYERS MAKE A LOT OF MONEY?
MONEY?

WHO CARES ABOUT MONEY?! THIS IS ART, YOU BLOCKHEAD!!
THIS IS GREAT MUSIC I'M PLAYING, AND PLAYING GREAT MUSIC IS AN ART!! DO YOU HEAR ME? AN ART!
ART! ART! ART! ART! ART!
WHAM
WHAM
WHAM
WHAM
WHAM
YOU FASCINATE ME!

NOW'S THE TIME FOR A GOOD PASS PLAY!
ALL RIGHT, MEN, LET'S GET IN THERE THIS TIME, AND SMEAR 'EM!
NOW, LISTEN CAREFULLY
SCHROEDER HIKES THE BALL TO YOU, LINUS, AND YOU FADE BACK, AND THROW ME A LONG PASS..
NOW, ARE YOU SURE YOU UNDERSTAND?
OF COURSE, I UNDERSTAND!
WELL, I HOPE SO..

SIGNALS! THIRTY-THREE! EIGHTEEN! FORTY-NINE!
HIKE!
PASS IT!

CLOMP
ZOOM!

ZOOM!
WHOOSH!
ZOOM!
WOOSH!
WHOOSH!
WHOOSH!

GOOD GRIEF... WHERE IS IT?
THINGS LIKE THIS DRIVE ME CRAZY!
WHERE'S MY FURRY HAT?
I'LL FREEZE TO DEATH WITHOUT MY BIG FURRY HAT...

HEY, THERE IT IS... RIGHT IN THE MIDDLE OF THE FLOOR...

!

WELL, I GUESS I CAN ALWAYS WEAR SOMETHING ELSE...

SIGH
Z

IT'S HAPPENING, CHARLIE BROWN! IT'S HAPPENING JUST LIKE THEY SAID IT WOULD!!

OF COURSE, IT'S HAPPENING.. IT'S SNOWING..WHAT ELSE DID YOU EXPECT THIS TIME OF YEAR?

SNOWING?

GOOD GRIEF..I THOUGHT IT WAS THE FALLOUT!

?
POW!

WHAM!

POW!

I FEEL TORN BETWEEN THE DESIRE TO CREATE AND THE DESIRE TO DESTROY..

YOU AND YOUR INSULTS!
BOY, IF YOU WEREN'T A GIRL...
I OUGHTA SLUG YOU A GOOD ONE!
ALL RIGHT, CHARLIE BROWN! COME ON, AND TRY IT!
YOU'RE ALWAYS TALKING BIG! NOW, C'MON! TRY IT!!

FIGHT! FIGHT!
OH, GOOD GRIEF!
C'MON, CHARLIE BROWN! PUT 'EM UP!
FIGHT!
C'MON..I'M READY FOR YOU! PUT 'EM UP THERE!!
A PERSON SHOULDN'T HAVE TO LOSE ALL HIS PRIDE WHEN HE'S ONLY SIX YEARS OLD...

SIGH
LUCY... HOW LONG BEFORE MY COWBOY PROGRAM COMES ON?
PRETTY SOON..
SAY, YOU WANNA TRY TO GUESS A SECRET?
DADDY'S GOING TO TAKE US SKATING?
NOPE!
GRAMPA'S COMING OVER?
NOPE!
MOM MADE SOME DOUGHNUTS?

NOPE!
WE'RE ALL GOING TO THE SHOW?
NOPE!
I'M GOING TO GET SOME NEW SHOES?
NOPE!
TOMORROW IS MY BIRTHDAY?
NOPE!
GEE...
I GIVE UP... WHAT'S THE SECRET?
YOU'VE JUST MISSED YOUR PROGRAM!

Z

THE YOUNG AND THE OLD..
THE RICH AND THE POOR..
...YESTERDAY, TODAY, TOMORROW AND...

YOU WERE LISTENING TO ME, WEREN'T YOU?
OF COURSE, I WAS!
WELL, I'LL BE!
?
HOW ABOUT THAT?
I'M NOT USED TO HAVING SOMEBODY LISTEN TO WHAT I HAVE TO SAY!

PHOOEY!
WHAT DO YOU MEAN, 'PHOOEY'?
JUST WHAT I SAID! PHOOEY!
FOR GOODNESS SAKE, LINUS, STOP COMPLAINING!
WELL, GOOD GRIEF, HOW DOES IT LOOK TO HAVE TO HAVE MY SISTER TAG AFTER ME TO HELP ME HOLD ON TO A STUPID BALLOON?!
ALL RIGHT, I'LL TIE IT ON TO YOUR SHOELACE, AND YOU CAN TAKE CARE OF IT YOURSELF!
GOOD!
HEY, WAIT!

THAT WASN'T SO GOOD, WAS IT? I'LL TIE IT TO THIS SHIRT BUTTON, AND WE'LL SEE IF THAT WORKS BETTER
NOPE, I GUESS IT DOESN'T!
THIS TIME I'LL TIE IT TO YOUR COLLAR..THAT SHOULD WORK..
WHEW! WHAT A STRUGGLE! I'M GLAD WE GOT THAT STRAIGHTENED OUT..
WHOOPS
DON'T SAY A WORD! JUST DON'T SAY ANYTHING!!

SIX O'CLOCK AGAIN..
GOOD GRIEF!
I HATE IT WHEN IT'S TIME TO FEED SNOOPY!
I HATE IT!

I HATE IT!
I HATE IT!
I HATE IT!
SNOOPY!
SUPPERTIME!!
BREAD
ZOOM!
ZOOM!
GULP!
I JUST HATE IT!!

MY DAD IS TALLER THAN YOUR DAD..
MY DAD HAS BROADER SHOULDERS THAN YOUR DAD..
MY DAD IS BETTER LOOKING THAN YOUR DAD
YOUR DAD!! YOU'RE ALWAYS TALKING ABOUT YOUR DAD!!
MAYBE MY DAD ISN'T PERFECT, BUT I LIKE HIM ANYWAY!!
HE'S MY DAD, AND I LIKE HIM!!!

YOU'RE SCREAMING, CHARLIE BROWN..
I'M SORRY...I DIDN'T MEAN TO SCREAM..
I WAS ONLY TRYING TO SAY THAT I LIKE MY DAD FOR WHAT HE IS...HE'S MY DAD, AND I LIKE HIM...
THAT'S VERY COMMENDABLE, CHARLIE BROWN...YOU ARE TO BE CONGRATULATED ON YOUR LOYALTY..
THANK YOU
HOWEVER, MY DAD...
OH, GOOD GRIEF!

I WISH THAT
I LOOKED
REAL TOUGH..
I WONDER WHAT SOME
DOGS DO TO MAKE THEMSELVES
LOOK TOUGH?
FANGS!
BY GOLLY, THAT'S WHAT YOU HAVE TO HAVE IF YOU'RE GOING TO SCARE PEOPLE!
FANGS AND A REAL FIERCE EXPRESSION
HERE COMES THAT STUPID LINUS AND HIS EQUALLY STUPID SISTER.. I'LL SHOW 'EM THE OL' FANGS AND SCARE THE DAYLIGHTS OUT OF THEM!

SIGH

WHAT'S THAT, SCHROEDER?
THIS IS A NEW RECORDING OF BRAHMS' FOURTH SYMPHONY..
WHAT ARE YOU GOING TO DO WITH IT?
I'M GOING TO TAKE IT HOME, AND LISTEN TO IT..

YOU MEAN YOU'RE GOING TO DANCE TO IT?
NO, I'M JUST GOING TO LISTEN TO IT..
BRAHMS
ARE YOU GOING TO MARCH AROUND THE ROOM WHILE YOU LISTEN TO IT?
NO, I'M JUST GOING TO SIT, AND LISTEN TO IT..
BRAHMS
YOU MEAN YOU'RE GOING TO WHISTLE OR SING WHILE YOU LISTEN TO IT?
NO, I'M JUST GOING TO LISTEN TO IT..
BRAHMS
THAT'S THE MOST RIDICULOUS THING I'VE EVER HEARD!

!
I FOUND THEM!
I FOUND MY MITTENS! I FOUND MY MITTENS!
WHERE'S THE PIE?!
PIE? WHAT PIE?!
STORIES

I FOUND MY MITTENS! WHEN YOU FIND YOUR MITTENS, YOU'RE SUPPOSED TO GET SOME PIE!
STORIES
OH, DON'T BE SO STUPID!
MOTHER HASN'T MADE A PIE IN THREE WEEKS!
WHAT GOOD DOES IT DO TO FIND YOUR MITTENS IF YOU DON'T GET ANY PIE?

I CAN'T STAND IT! I JUST CAN'T STAND IT!
YOU STUPID TREE! LET GO OF THAT KITE!
LET GO, I SAY, OR I'LL GIVE YOU THE WORST SHAKING YOU'VE EVER HAD!

IS IT AUTUMN?

OH, NO! LOOK WHO'S COMING... "PIG-PEN," THE HUMAN DUST-BOWL!
GOOD MORNING, VIOLET...'MORNING, CHARLIE BROWN..
"PIG-PEN" IS THE ONLY PERSON I KNOW WHO CAN RAISE A CLOUD OF DUST ON A CLEAN SIDEWALK!
AAK!! KOFF! KOFF!

Z
?
!
GOOD GRIEF! I THOUGHT I HAD BEEN BURIED ALIVE!

!
"RAIN, RAIN, GO AWAY.. COME AGAIN SOME OTHER DAY !!"

I SAID "RAIN, RAIN, GO AWAY.. COME AGAIN SOME OTHER DAY !!!"
YOU'RE NOT LISTENING!

WAIT 'TIL I WIND IT UP..
THERE..NOW, LISTEN..
ISN'T THAT BEAUTIFUL?
THAT WAS 'ROCK-A-BYE, BABY.'.. I BROUGHT IT OVER JUST SO YOU COULD HEAR IT!
WELL! THAT WAS VERY NICE..

YOU SHOULD HAVE A MUSIC-BOX, SCHROEDER..
?
!
TOCCATA AND FUGUE In D MINOR BY BACH
I MIGHT HAVE KNOWN..

GULP
SNOOPY'S THE ONLY DOG IN THE WORLD WHO CAN RETRIEVE A SOAP-BUBBLE..

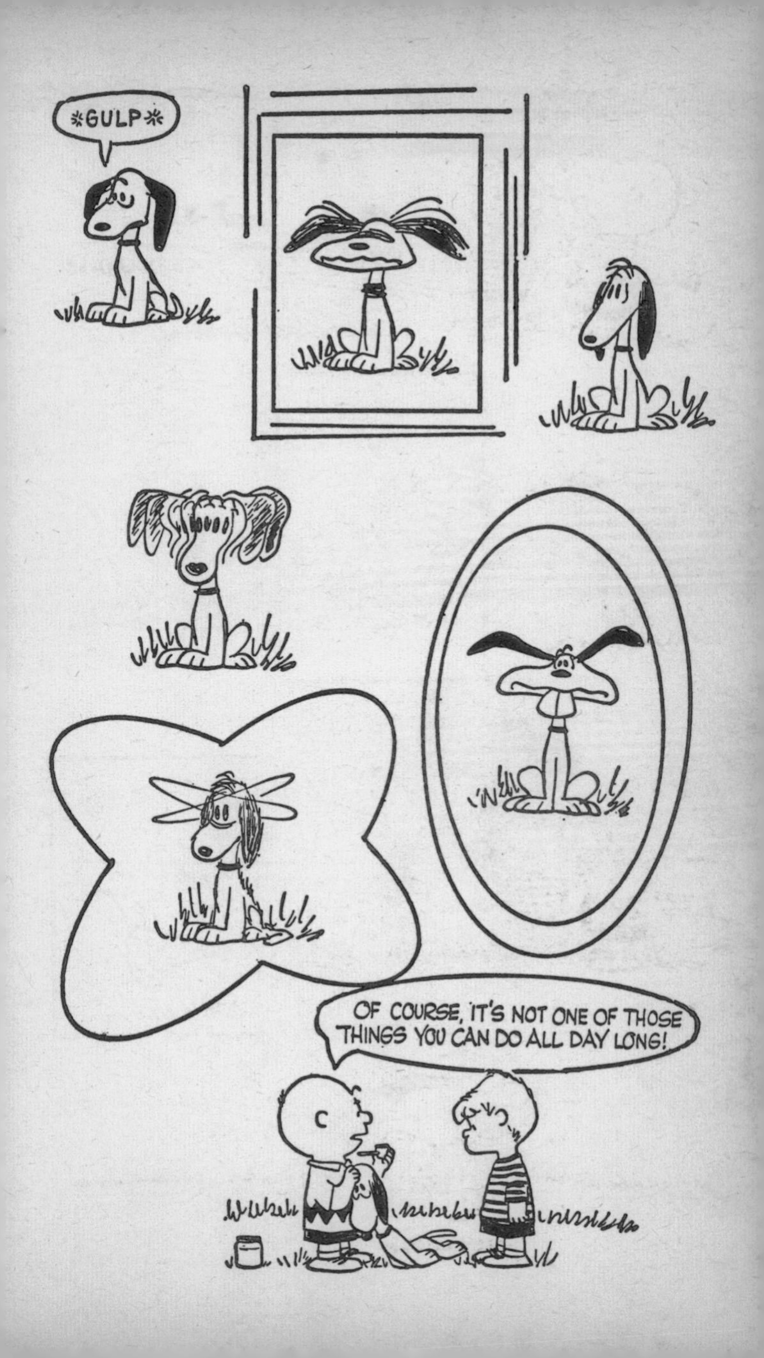
GULP
OF COURSE, IT'S NOT ONE OF THOSE THINGS YOU CAN DO ALL DAY LONG!

DO YOU KNOW ANYTHING ABOUT MULES?
I'VE BEEN READING ABOUT THEM..
Z
THEY SAY THAT THE MULE IS A VERY POWERFUL ANIMAL..
Z
THAT'S TRUE... I'VE HEARD THAT THEY CAN ACTUALLY KICK DOWN BARN DOORS!

KICK DOWN BARN DOORS?
UH, HUH..
THAT'S FANTASTIC!
I KNOW IT IS, BUT IT'S TRUE!
RIDICULOUS!

Z
Z
Z

Z
GOOD GRIEF!

YELL AT IT, CHARLIE BROWN..
WELL, GO AHEAD..
YOU STUPID TREE! LET GO OF THAT KITE!!
YELL AT IT AGAIN..
YOU STUPID TREE! LET GO OF THAT KITE!

NOW GRAB IT, AND SHAKE IT!!
SHAKE IT HARDER..
ARGH!
NOW KICK IT!
WHAM
WHY DO YOU DO EVERYTHING I TELL YOU?

?
I DON'T WANT TO WATCH THAT PROGRAM..I WANT TO WATCH THIS PROGRAM!
CLICK!
YAUGHH!
BANG! BANG! BANG! BANG! BANG! BANG!
Grrrowrr!

POW! POW! POW!
SIGH

YIPE!
AAK!
ZOOOMM!
GOOD GRIEF!
ZOOM!
IF HE DOES THAT ONCE MORE, HE'S GOING TO DRIVE ME CRAZY!
WHY DON'T WE TEACH HIM A LESSON?
WE'LL PUT THE WICKETS REAL CLOSE TO THE GROUND, LIKE THIS...

NOW, THE NEXT TIME HE TRIES TO ZOOM THROUGH... WHAM!
I CAN SEE IT NOW! HE'LL COME SAILING ALONG, AND POW!
SURE...IT CAN'T MISS.. HE'LL COME ROARING ACROSS THE LAWN, AND BAM!!
HERE HE COMES!
I CAN'T LOOK!!
ZOOM!
hop
SIGH!

THAT STUPID KITE WENT DOWN AGAIN!
KITES DRIVE ME CRAZY!
I'VE NEVER SEEN ONE YET THAT DIDN'T GET ITSELF ALL TANGLED UP IN EVERYTHING.. EXCUSE ME..
?
I WONDER WHERE THAT FOOL THING WENT DOWN?

HOW I HATE KITES!! I'LL NEVER BUY ANOTHER ONE AS LONG AS I LIVE!!!
EXCUSE ME...
I HATE EVERY BONE IN THAT KITE'S BODY!
GOOD GRIEF!! WHAT A MESS!
SO THAT'S WHERE YOU CAME DOWN, EH? GOOD!
BURN, YOU MONSTER!!

YOU KNOW WHAT?
WHAT?
NINETY-TWO, NINETY-THREE, NINETY-FOUR..
IT SAYS HERE THAT THE YOUTH OF TODAY IS BADLY OUT OF CONDITION..
..NINETY-FIVE!
...NINETY-SIX, NINETY-SEVEN, NINETY-EIGHT, NINETY-NINE..

ONE HUNDRED!
ONE HUNDRED AN' ONE, ONE HUNDRED AN' TWO, ONE HUNDRED AN' THREE, ONE HUNDRED AN' FOUR, ONE HUNDRED AN' FIVE..
FIRST WITH THE LEFT, AND THEN WITH THE RIGHT... ONE HUNDRED AN' SIX, ONE HUNDRED AN' SEVEN, ONE HUNDRED AN' EIGHT..
I DON'T KNOW ABOUT YOUTH, BUT WE LITTLE KIDS ARE IN GREAT SHAPE!

Z

POPCORN
HERE, SNOOPY...JUST TO SHOW YOU THAT MY HEART IS IN THE RIGHT PLACE, I'M GOING TO GIVE YOU A WHOLE PIECE OF POPCORN!
CHOMP CHOMP CHOMP

CRUNCH CRUNCH
CHOMP CHOMP
CRUNCH
?
CHOMP CHOMP CHOMP
CHOMP CHOMP
POPCORN
CHOMP CHOMP CHOMP
CRUNCH CRUNCH
CHOMP
CRUNCH
CHOMP
CHOMP
CHOMP
CHOMP
IF IT WERE ANYONE ELSE, I'D THINK IT WAS CAREFUL CHEWING... WITH HIM I KNOW IT'S SARCASM!

LUCY!
LUCY, THERE'S A PORCUPINE IN OUR YARD!
A PORCUPINE? WHAT WAS IT DOING?
NOTHING.. IT WAS JUST LOOKING AT ME..

SEE? IT JUST SITS THERE LOOKING AT ME..
THAT'S NOT A PORCUPINE! THAT'S JUST A BUSH!
OH...
GOOD GRIEF!
STOP LOOKING AT ME!

?
ZOOM!
ZOOM!

AAUGH!
YOU DRIVE ME CRAZY!

WHOOPS!

WHAM!
WHEW!
SEE WHAT YOU MADE ME DO?!

THE WHOLE TROUBLE WITH YOU IS YOU NEVER LISTEN!
YOU'RE CRAZY!
ALL YOU EVER DO IS TALK!
YOU'RE CRAZY!
I'M RIGHT, AND YOU'RE WRONG! IT'S AS SIMPLE AS THAT!
YOU'RE CRAZY!
OH, YEAH? WELL, LET'S GO HOME RIGHT NOW AND LOOK IN THE DICTIONARY! WE'LL SEE WHO'S CRAZY!

BUT JUST REMEMBER THIS, CHARLIE BROWN...
IF I'M RIGHT, I GET 'HITS' ON YOU!!
'HIT'S'? WHAT IN THE WORLD IS THAT?!
IF I'M RIGHT, I GET TO HIT YOU ON THE ARM!
WELL, WHAT IF I'M RIGHT?! WHAT THEN?!!
THEN YOU GET TO HIT LINUS...

HERE COMES THE FIERCE TIGER SNEAKING UP ON THE HELPLESS CHILD...
SUDDENLY HE POUNCES!

SUDDENLY HE POUNCES!
RATS!

Z
TICKLE
TICKLE
TICKLE
TICKLE TICKLE
TICKLE TICKLE
HEE HEE
HEE HEE
HEE

OH, NOT ON THE FEET! OH, NO! PLEASE! NOT ON THE FEET!!
HEE HEE HEE
TICKLE! TICKLE! TICKLE!
HEE HEE HEE HEE HEE HEE
OH, MAN! I'M EXHAUSTED! OH, MY RIBS! OH, MAN! WHEW
I HAVEN'T LAUGHED SO MUCH IN A YEAR.. WHAT A GIRL! WOW!
IT MUST BE NICE TO BE ABLE TO BRING SO MUCH HAPPINESS INTO SOMEONE'S LIFE..

THE REASON I CAN GUARANTEE THIS PARACHUTE, CHARLIE BROWN, IS THAT I MADE IT MYSELF..
THIS IS A GOOD HEAVY BLANKET, AND THESE ARE VERY STOUT ROPES..
PUT MY CAP ON FOR ME, WILL YOU?

THERE..NOW, ALL YOU HAVE TO DO IS JUMP OFF THAT STUMP, AND FLOAT GENTLY TO THE GROUND..
JUST WHAT I WAS AFRAID OF.. HE'S GETTING COLD FEET...
GERONIMO!
WUMP!
MMGBMM MGMMBM MMGMM
I THINK I'D BETTER GO HOME, AN' SEE WHAT'S ON T.V.

BEETHOVEN! PHOOEY! HE WASN'T SO GREAT!
WHAT DO YOU MEAN, HE WASN'T SO GREAT?!

WELL, HE DIDN'T GET TO BE KING, DID HE? HUH?
HE DIDN'T GET TO BE KING, DID HE? HUH? DID HE???
DID HE GET TO BE KING? HUH? DID HE? DID HE?!!
GOOD GRIEF!
HOW CAN ANYONE BE CALLED 'GREAT' IF HE DOESN'T GET TO BE KING?

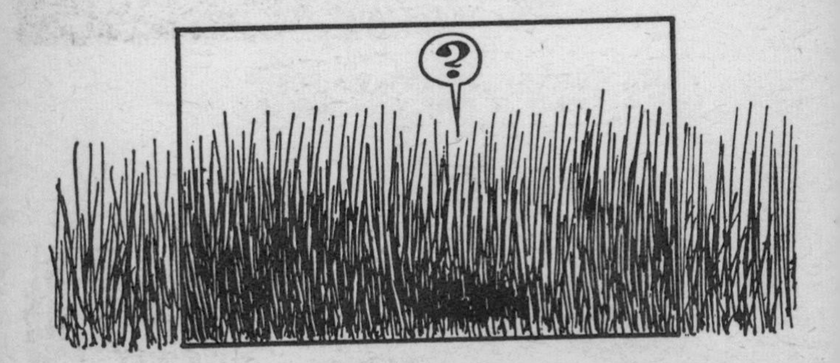

!
!
WHEN YOU HAVE CLAUSTROPHOBIA, YOU LEARN TO WALK ON TOP OF THE WEEDS!

CRUNCH
CHOMP
CHOMP
CHOMP
CRUNCH

CHOMP CHOMP CHOMP
CHOMP CHOMP CHOMP

IS THAT YOUR HEAD, CHARLIE BROWN, OR IS THE MOON OUT EARLY TODAY?
BOY, YOU SURE THINK YOU'RE SMART, DON'T YOU?
I OUGHTA SOCK YOU RIGHT ON THE NOSE!
YOU CAN'T HIT ME, CHARLIE BROWN! I'M A GIRL!

NYAHH!!!
NYAH NYAH NYAH NYAH!
?
HERE, NOW! YOU STOP THAT! STOP THAT, I SAY!!
YOU STOP KICKING OUR HOUSE!
SCHULZ

OH, GOOD GRIEF! NOT AGAIN!
I CAN'T STAND IT..
KITE CAUGHT IN THE SAME TREE AGAIN, EH, CHARLIE BROWN?
WHY DON'T YOU LET ME YELL AT IT? WILL YOU LET ME YELL AT IT FOR YOU, CHARLIE BROWN?

I DON'T CARE WHAT YOU DO! YOU CAN YELL AT IT 'TIL YOUR HEAD FALLS OFF AS FAR AS I'M CONCERNED...
GOOD
!
YOU STUPID KITE! COME DOWN OUT OF THAT TREE!!!

OH, OH!
HERE IT COMES!
HEY! WHERE'S EVERYBODY GOING?
HOME! IT'S RAINING YOU BLOCKHEAD!
COME BACK HERE!
THIS IS ONLY A SPRING SHOWER!

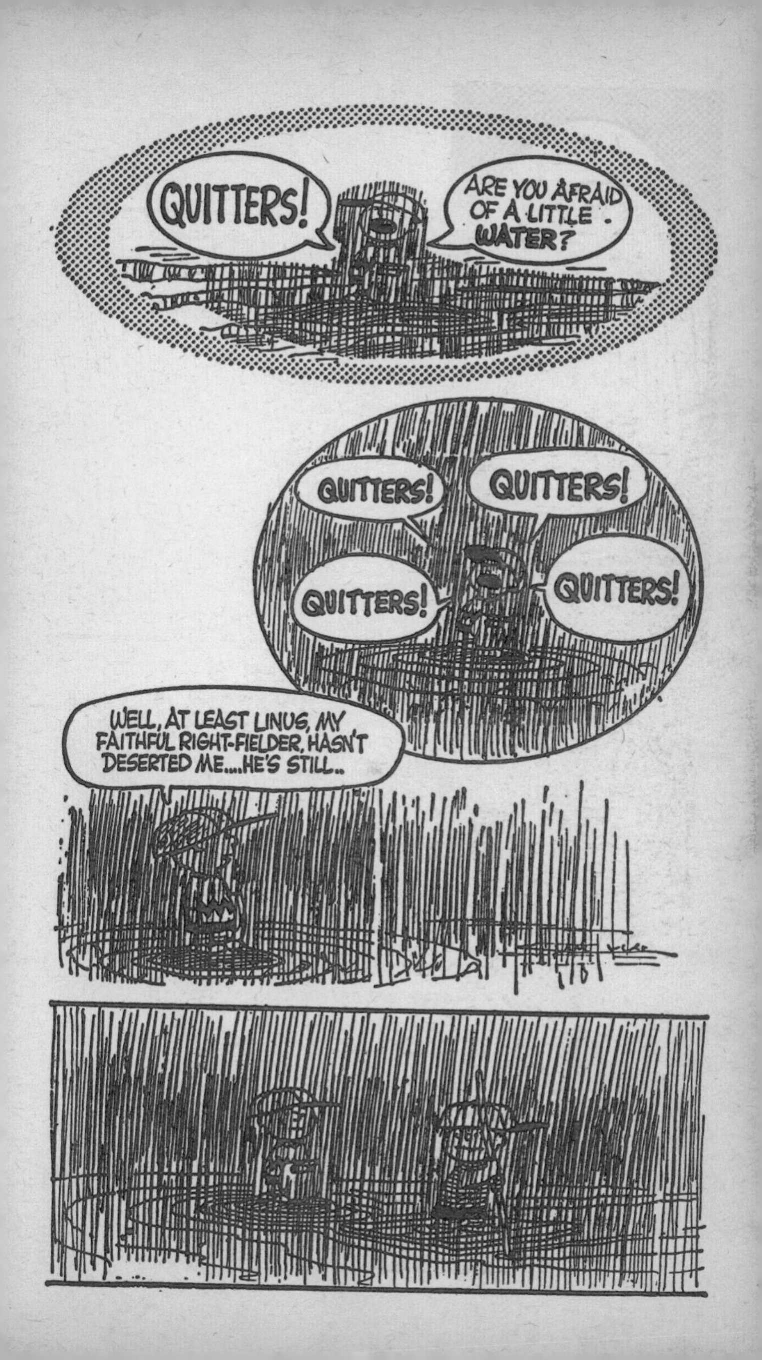
QUITTERS!
ARE YOU AFRAID OF A LITTLE WATER?
QUITTERS!
QUITTERS!
QUITTERS!
QUITTERS!
WELL, AT LEAST LINUS, MY FAITHFUL RIGHT-FIELDER, HASN'T DESERTED ME....HE'S STILL..

WHAT'S GOING ON HERE?
WHOOSH
ZOOM
I GUESS I KNEW I'D NEVER GET AWAY WITH IT..

HERE, SNOOPY... CHASE THE BALL...
!

WHAM!
WHEW WHAT A BLOW!
HERE, KID
THIS IS RETRIEVING?

FOOEY!
'FOOEY' IS RIGHT!
FLIP
SHE'S HOPELESS, CHARLIE BROWN..
WHY DO WE HAVE TO LET HER PLAY?!
DON'T WORRY ABOUT IT... SHE'LL GET DISCOURAGED RIGHT AWAY, AND GO HOME..
!
BLIP!

RATS!
SEE? SHE'S DISCOURAGED ALREADY...NOW SHE WON'T BOTHER US ANY MORE..
OH, NO!
WHAT'S THE MATTER?
WHAM!
"SEE? SHE'S DISCOURAGED ALREADY...NOW SHE WON'T BOTHER US ANY MORE.."

SCHULZ

LUCY, HAVE YOU SEEN LINUS?
HE'S DOWN THERE BY THE WATER, THROWING STONES...

EVERY TIME WE COME TO THE BEACH, HE SPENDS THE WHOLE DAY THROWING STONES INTO THE WATER..

HAVING FUN, LINUS?

SORT OF...

WHAT DO YOU MEAN, 'SORT OF'?

I HAVE A HARD TIME GETTING ANY DISTANCE..

OH, NO!!!
THIS IS THE LAST STRAW!
DID YOU DRAW THIS PICTURE IN MY BOOK?
I GUESS I DID.....
IT'S A PRETTY NICE PICTURE, DON'T YOU THINK? SEE, THERE'S A KNIGHT ON HORSEBACK AND THERE'S A BIG DRAGON, AND...
WHO DO YOU THINK YOU ARE?

WHAT CAN I SAY?
THIS IS MY BOOK, AND YOU HAVE DRAWN A PICTURE IN IT... NOW, I WANT TO KNOW WHAT YOU'RE GOING TO DO ABOUT IT!
Furry Tails
DO YOU WANT ME TO SIGN IT?
I THINK I SAID THE WRONG THING!
BONK!

SAY! I THOUGHT WE WERE GONNA TAKE TURNS USING THAT UMBRELLA?

WELL, WE WERE, BUT I'VE DECIDED THAT AS LONG AS YOU'RE ALL WET ALREADY, THERE'S REALLY NO SENSE IN MY GIVING YOU THE UMBRELLA AND THEN GETTING WET, TOO...
THAT WOULDN'T MAKE SENSE, WOULD IT? NO, IT WOULDN'T...
SO MUCH IN THIS WORLD DEPENDS UPON WHO GETS BORN FIRST!

WAP!
RUN IT OUT, LINUS! RUN IT OUT!
?
FIRST I GOTTA HAVE MY BLANKET..

STOMP
WHAM
YOU'RE OUT!!
I CAN'T STAND IT...
SCHULZ

GET AWAY FROM THOSE CRAYONS!!
MOM!
OH, GOOD GRIEF!!
LUCY! YOU SHARE THOSE CRAYONS WITH YOUR BROTHER!

BOY, I OUGHTA SLUG YOU A GOOD ONE!
JUST GIVE ME THE CRAYONS..
HERE'S THREE OF 'EM... NOW, GET OUTA HERE!
♪
I GAVE HIM THREE, MOM.. WAS THAT ENOUGH?
THAT WAS FINE, LUCY.. IT'S ALWAYS NICE TO SHARE YOUR THINGS...
WHITE, GRAY AND BLACK *SIGH*

ZZ
AHEM
THAT'S MY BLANKET YOU'RE SLEEPING ON, YOU STUPID DOG!

YAWN!
Z
HEY! WHO LET ALL THOSE CATS IN HERE?

MMMMM
MMMMM
OOOOOOOOO...
SIGH
CHOPIN!